# ALEX CF'S

# PUNKS IN THE WILLOWS

Dedicated to the punks who inspired my political and creative endeavours,
and to those I have been fortunate to share those endeavours with.

What kind of animal is punk rock?
The elusive, eccentric, perhaps hard to spot
A many and varied assortment of folk
Of different communities and cultures of note

Their music can be aggressive and angry and fast
D-beats and blast beats in songs that don't last
Light and melodic, heavy and slow
Or lack any obvious music at all

Punk rock might be music, but for punks, it's much more
An ideal based on friendship, and above all
Creativity, social justice, equality
It is noise with a message, a message of peace!

But why all this anger if punk is so kind?
That anger is aimed at those who make life
Difficult, unfair, for greed and for war
Governments and religions who want to control

Punk is expression, hearts worn on their sleeves
The bands that they love, and beliefs held dear
With patches and badges and battle jackets
Adorned and embellish with passion they stitch

Dyed hair, spiked hair, matted or shaved
Piercings and tattoos that help to reclaim
A sense of themselves from their feelings of doubt
Their bodies, their minds and a place in this world

Like all other animals, punks have differing views
Not every punk thinks like another might do
One size doesn't always fit every punk
And what counts as important, to another might not

Some punks are hopeful, and want to make change
Some punks are nihilists, and they're future afraid
Some punks are musicians, drums, bass and guitar!
Some punks have hard times that shape who they are

Differently abled or neurodiverse
They all sing together, every chorus and verse
They celebrate variety above everything else
It is here that they find their defining purpose

Some punk is ska, some punk is metal
Some punk is avant garde, some instrumental
Punk is a tool with which to say
The things that they care about, the reason they play

Some punks drink and take recreational drugs
Some claim straight edge, and like to 'X up'
Some like to party and stay up all night
Some like to read books with early bed times

Punks like to bake and make and do things
Bike rides, forage fungi, perhaps write zines
Punks like to sew, or learn useful skills
Some like to squat, they don't have to pay bills

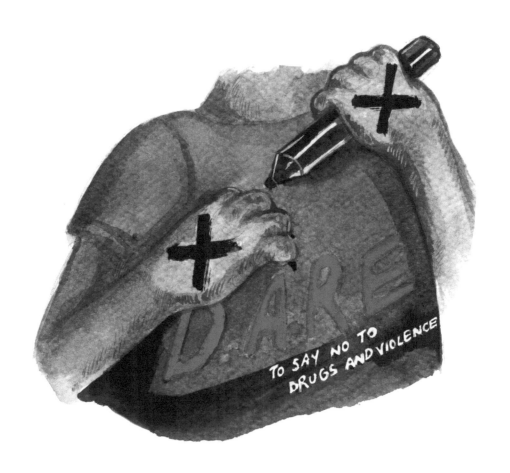

Some punks are vegan, for animal rights
Stand against racism, fascism and fight
They fight for habitats, to halt climate change
Try to lessen the impact that we have all made

Some punks are anarchists - against power's misuse
Libertarian socialist decentralised views
Tear down the systems of oppressive control
And create a fairer, autonomous world.

Punks join together with all walks of life
Protest in the streets for equal rights
They will fight for the oppressed, and the marginalised
Add their voice to the voiceless and stand as allies

Lesbian, gay, transgender and queer punks
Indigenous, black, punks of colour
There are punk parents and carers, and folks who adopt
There are those that want children and those who do not

Punk rock is a rebellion
One of righteous fury and political dissent
But also of love and equality
For the want of a world where all are free

Punk is not defined by the sum of its parts
Punks are not perfect, but they've at least made a start
Through learning and growth and good intentions
Punk is an animal true to its word

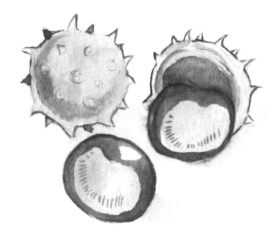

Alex CF is an illustrator, author and sculptor. His work revolves around animal mythology and political fantasy, having written the environmental epic, 'The Books of Orata' - 'Seek The Throat From Which We Sing' and 'Wretched Is The Husk' and the illustrated companion book, 'The Orata, A Compendium Of The Cultures And Creeds Of Naa.' His personal and political aspirations are explored further in 'The Book Of Venym, An Egalitarian Demonology.' An illustrated anti-fascist occult grimoire, a call to arms in the defence of nature and against humanities proclivities for violence, told through striking illustrations of benevolent demons and deities.

Alex has been involved in DIY punk, animal rights and alternative culture for much of his adult life, and is the vocalist in a number of bands, where he creates self contained narratives and artwork inspired by his favourite authors, and ideologies shared within the band. He was the vocalist in Fall of Efrafa, and is currently involved in many musical projects.

You can purchase Alex's other titles at
alexcf.bigcartel.com